STOCKING STUMPERS

PHILADELPHIA PHILLIES

By S. Claus

RED-LETTER PRESS, INC.
Saddle River, New Jersey

STOCKING STUMPERS - PHILADELPHIA PHILLIES
Copyright ©2013 Red-Letter Press, Inc.
ISBN-10: 1-60387-016-4
ISBN-13: 978-1-60387-016-0

Red-Letter Press, Inc.
P.O. Box 393, Saddle River, NJ 07458
www.Red-LetterPress.com
info@Red-LetterPress.com

ACKNOWLEDGMENTS
SANTA'S SUBORDINATE CLAUSES

Compiled By:
Steve Fiorentine

Editor:
Jack Kreismer

Contributor:
Jeff Kreismer

Cover Design:
Cliff Behum

Special Mention:
Sparky Anderson Kreismer

Introduction

Whether you're having a few quiet
moments to yourself or enjoying a
reunion with friends and family, Stocking
Stumpers is the perfect holiday companion.
Gather 'round the Christmas tree or simply
kick back in your easy chair while
trying out the holiday humdingers,
tailor-made tests and trivia tidbits.

Once you've had a sampling, I think you'll
agree, Stocking Stumpers is proof of the
Christmas pudding that good things do
come in small packages. Ho ho ho!

Merry Christmas!!

S. Claus

The Mantle Meter

'Tis right around Christmas
and all through the book,

There are all sorts of stumpers
everywhere that you look.

There are quizzes and seasonal tests
to take you to task,

But what are those "stocking"
questions you ask?

Well, the stockings are hung
by the chimney with care.

The more that are filled,
the tougher the bear.

And so it is that
the Mantle Meter keeps score,

Rating the stumpers,
one stocking or more.

STOCKING
STUMPERS

PHILADELPHIA
PHILLIES

FIRST PITCH

1. What pitcher has the most Opening Day starts in Phillies history?

2. As the visiting team in 1935, the Phillies took on the Cincinnati Reds at Crosley Field in a Major League Baseball first of its kind. What?

3. The Phillies set a benchmark for futility in 2007 when they became the first team in professional sports to lose how many games in their history?

4. What Phillies switch-hitter not known for his power became the first player in team history to homer from both sides of the plate in the same game in 1989?

5. In 2001, who became the first Phillie to join the 30-30 club, by collecting both 30 home runs and 30 stolen bases in a single season?

In the second inning of Game 2 of the 2008 NLDS against the Milwaukee Brewers, what player hit the first postseason grand slam in Phillies history off of ace CC Sabathia?

ANSWERS

1.

Steve Carlton (14 openers)

2.

Night game

3.

10,000

4.

Steve Jeltz

5.

Bobby Abreu

Shane Victorino

HISTORY 101

1. From 1883 until 1890, when the team officially adopted the Phillies moniker, the Phillies were called what other name simultaneously?

2. In 1894, the Phillies outfield consisted of three future Hall of Famers who all finished the season with batting averages above .400. Can you name any one of them?

3. The Phillies home from 1938-1970 might have been called Cornelius McGillicuddy Stadium if not for what reason?

4. The Phillies clinched their first National League pennant in 1915 but ended up losing in the World Series to what American League team: Red Sox, Rangers or Angels?

5. Although they were upset by the St. Louis Cardinals in the NLDS, the 2011 Phillies hold the franchise record for wins in a regular season. How many victories did they record?

The Phillies are the only team in Major League Baseball to have what sewn on their uniform sleeve?

ANSWERS

1.

Philadelphia Quakers

2.

Ed Delahanty,
Billy Hamilton and Sam Thompson

3.

Cornelius McGillicuddy changed his
name to the legendary Connie Mack.

4.

Boston Red Sox

5.

102

The players' uniform numbers

MANAGER MANIA

1.
The Phillies won World Series championships in 1980 and 2008 under the tutelage of what two managers?

2.
Who has managed and won the most Phillies games?

3.
In 2001, who became the only Phillies skipper (a former player known for his hot temper), to be named the NL Manager of the Year?

4.
Name the Phillies skipper from 1997-2000 who went on to win two World Series titles with the Red Sox.

5.
Besides Charlie Manuel, who is the only other Phillies manager to guide Philadelphia to the postseason three times?

What Phillies pitcher had a career day on June 23, 1971, when he belted two home runs in addition to tossing a no-hitter against the Cincinnati Reds?

ANSWERS

1.

Dallas Green and Charlie Manuel

2.

Charlie Manuel

3.

Larry Bowa

4.

Terry Francona

5.

Danny Ozark

Rick Wise

THE WHIZ KIDS

1. The 1950 NL pennant came down to the last game of the season between the Phillies and Brooklyn Dodgers featuring a showdown between what two All-Star pitchers?

2. With the game tied 1-1 in the bottom of the ninth inning, what Phillie's throw from center field nailed Brooklyn's Cal Abrams at home plate to keep the score tied?

3. Whose go-ahead three-run homer in the top of the tenth inning set up the Phillies for their second World Series trip in team history?

4. In the Fall Classic, the young Phillies were no match for their seasoned opponents. They were swept by what team in the midst of a streak of five consecutive World Series titles?

5. In a riff on the 1950 Phillies nickname, Philadelphia's 1983 aging veteran roster was jokingly referred to as what?

❄ SEASONAL STUMPER ❄

The name of the most prominent chipmunk in that yuletide song is the same as the first name of what third baseman who the Phillies received from the Chicago Cubs as part of a package for franchise icon Richie Ashburn in 1960?

ANSWERS

1.

Robin Roberts and Don Newcombe

2.

Richie Ashburn

3.

Dick Sisler

4.

New York Yankees

5.

The Wheeze Kids

Seasonal Stumper Answer:

Alvin Dark

THE ACE

1. In the final eight days of the 1950 season, how many starts did Robin Roberts make to lead the Phillies to the National League pennant?

2. Roberts, known for exceptional stamina, once pitched how many consecutive complete games from 1952-53: 14, 21 or 28?

3. Beginning in 1950, how many consecutive 20 win seasons did Roberts rattle off: 3, 6, or 9?

4. Roberts is tied with what other two pitchers for the most starts in All-Star Game history with five? (Hint: Their nicknames are "Big D" and "Lefty".)

5. Roberts' Phillies number was retired before a 1962 spring training game in which he pitched for what visiting team (a club he'd never play for during the regular season)?

The Phillies have played what team five out of the nine times they have appeared in the NLCS?

ANSWERS

1.

Five

2.

28

3.

Six

4.

Don Drysdale and
Vernon "Lefty" Gomez

5.

New York Yankees

Los Angeles Dodgers

THE ONE AND ONLY

1. What Phillie is the only relief pitcher ever to be awarded the National League MVP?

2. Who is the only Phillies closer to record a perfect season by converting all 41 of his save opportunities, while going another seven for seven in the playoffs?

3. What player is the only Phillie to hit more than 50 home runs in a single season?

4. Who is the only player to wear a #0 Phillies jersey?

5. In 2010, what Phillies pitcher became the only player to hurl a shutout in four separate decades?

Terry Mullholland and Kevin Millwood fired the only two no-hitters in Veterans Stadium history. Against what team did both no-hitters occur?

ANSWERS

1.
Jim Konstanty

2.
Brad Lidge

3.
Ryan Howard

4.
Al Oliver

5.
Jamie Moyer

San Francisco Giants

1980 WORLD SERIES

1. Whose game-winning RBI double in the top of the 10th inning of Game 5 of the 1980 NLCS against the Houston Astros sent the Phillies to their first World Series in 30 years?

2. In an early 4-0 hole to the Kansas City Royals in Game 1, what player hit a three-run home run in the bottom of the third to give Philadelphia its first lead of the Series?

3. What Royal sat out the final few innings of Game 2 because of hemorrhoids, had minor surgery to return to action and then declared, "My problems are all behind me"?

4. What Phillie, in the right place at the right time with the bases loaded in the top of the ninth of Game 6, caught a deflected pop-up off the mitt of catcher Bob Boone?

5. With the bases loaded and two outs, who struck out Kansas City's Willie Wilson for a then World Series record 12th time to clinch the Phillies first World Series title?

Steve Carlton picked up the win in the 1980 World Series-clinching Game 6. However, in Game 2, Carlton was at the center of controversy when umpires made him do what after receiving complaints from the Kansas City dugout?

ANSWERS

1.

Garry Maddox

2.

Bake McBride

3.

George Brett

4.

Pete Rose

5.

Tug McGraw

Carlton was forced to wash his hands after being accused of doctoring the ball with a foreign substance.

THE RECORD BOOKS

1. What Phillies Hall of Famer set the record for runs scored in a single season with 198 in 1894: Billy Hamilton, Earl Hamilton or Jack Hamilton?

2. As part of an MVP-winning season in 2007, what Phillie set a new major league record for at-bats in a single season with 716?

3. Who passed fellow Phillies pitcher Robin Roberts in 2010 for the dubious record of most home runs allowed in a career?

4. Who tied a World Series record by launching five home runs during Philadelphia's 2009 World Series appearance versus the New York Yankees?

5. In 1961, the Phillies reached an all-time low point by losing a modern day major league record of how many consecutive games: 18, 23, or 28?

❄ SEASONAL STUMPER ❄

On Christmas Eve in 1969, what player challenged MLB's reserve clause by writing a letter to commissioner Bowie Kuhn protesting his trade from the Cardinals to the Phillies?

ANSWERS

1.
Billy Hamilton
(The other two Hamiltons were Phillies,
but not exactly Hall of Fame material.)

2.

Jimmy Rollins

3.

Jamie Moyer

4.

Chase Utley

5.

23

Seasonal Stumper Answer:

Curt Flood- Though his challenge was
unsuccessful and he was eventually traded to another
club, Flood's protest paved the way for free agency.

TWO OF A KIND

1. Omar Oivares, in 1995, and Rick White, in 2006, are the only two Phillies to wear what double uniform number?

2. What Phillie took home two postseason awards in 2008 when he was named both the NLCS and World Series MVP?

3. Who are the two Phillies to be crowned Home Run Derby champions, which happened to occur consecutively in 2005 and 2006?

4. Who are the only two Phillies catchers to be recognized for their defense with Gold Glove Awards?

5. Andy Ashby, in 1991, and Juan Perez, in 2011, are the only Phillies to pitch an immaculate inning. What is an immaculate inning?

In 1979, what Phillie tied Lee Lacey's record for consecutive pinch hit appearances with a home run when he blasted 3 straight homers coming off of the bench?

ANSWERS

1.

00

2.

Cole Hamels

3.

Bobby Abreu and Ryan Howard

4.

Bob Boone and Mike Lieberthal

5.

Striking out three
batters on nine pitches

Del Unser

A GLOBAL GAME

1. What former Phillies shortstop from Vera Cruz, Mexico, has a son who is a current big league general manager?

2. In 2010, what catcher became the first native of Panama to catch a perfect game when he was behind the dish for Roy Halladay's perfecto?

3. What country did Bobby Abreu represent in the 2005 Home Run Derby when he set a Derby record with 41 total long balls?

4. What player who pitched for the Phillies from 1965-66 is the only Canadian-born player inducted into the National Baseball Hall of Fame?

5. Who became the first Asian-born player to suit up for the Phillies in 2007?

What Phillies player holds the record for highest batting average in a League Championship Series, hitting .778 in 10 plate appearances during the 1976 NLCS?

ANSWERS

1.

Ruben Amaro, whose son Ruben Jr., of course, is the GM of the Phillies

2.

Carlos Ruiz

3.

Venezuela

4.

Ferguson Jenkins

5.

Tadahito Iguchi

Jay Johnstone

PUTT-PUTT

1. Richie Ashburn accumulated more hits in the 1950s than anyone else in Major League Baseball. Did Ashburn ever win a National League Batting title?

2. Ashburn batted above .300 in how many of his 15 major league seasons: 9, 12, or 15?

3. Ashburn became an original member of what National League team in 1962?

4. Which was longer, Ashburn's playing career or broadcasting career with the Phillies?

5. The centerfield area of Citizens Bank Park that contains the Philadelphia Baseball Wall of Fame is named in honor of the Phillies icon. What's it called?

Can you name the first baseman who barely survived being shot by a crazed woman in 1949 and returned to the Phillies the next year to help the Whiz Kids win the pennant?

ANSWERS

1.

Yes, twice- 1955 and 1958.

2.

Nine

3.

The New York Mets

4.

Broadcasting- Ashburn was in the booth
from 1963 until the day he died, in 1997.

5.

Ashburn Alley

Eddie Waitkus

Screen Test

1. Phillies teammates Mike Lieberthal, Doug Glanville and Pat Burrell appeared in what 2001 movie based on the Cape Cod Baseball League?

2. Phillies sluggers Ryan Howard and Chase Utley made cameos in an episode of what television series that takes place in the City of Brotherly Love?

3. Mike Schmidt, Larry Bowa, Garry Maddox, Dick Ruthven and Del Unser competed together as a team on what TV game show following their 1980 World Series victory?

4. In 1997, what two Phillies made appearances as themselves in a *Saturday Night Live* skit?

5. What native-Hawaiian Phillie guest-starred on an episode of *Hawaii Five-O*?

❄ Seasonal stumper ❄

As the elves were loading gifts on Santa's sleigh two days before Christmas in 1993, the Phillies were exchanging presents with the Cubs. The Phils swapped shortstop Mickey Morandini to Chicago for what outfielder who would play the next six years for Philly?

ANSWERS

1.

Summer Catch

2.

It's Always Sunny in Philadelphia

3.

Family Feud

4.

Scott Rolen and Gregg Jefferies

5.

Shane Victorino

Seasonal Stumper Answer:

Doug Glanville

BLOCKBUSTERS

1. The Phillies acquired what pitcher, who went on to become an NLCS MVP and three-time All-Star for the team, from the Astros in 1992 for reliever Jason Grimsley?

2. In December of 2009, the Phillies acquired what Cy Young Award winner from the Toronto Blue Jays and dealt what other Cy Young winner to the Seattle Mariners?

3. In a trade the franchise would regret for years, the Phillies dealt what future Hall of Famer to the Cubs, along with Larry Bowa, for journeyman shortstop Ivan Dejesus?

4. What one-time Phillies prospect and future All-Star was acquired from the White Sox in 2005 and then sent back to Chicago a year later as part of a package for Freddy Garcia?

5. Who became the target of frequent boos from Philly fans after he demanded a trade and was dealt to the Cardinals for Placido Polanco, Bud Smith and Mike Timlin?

What future multiple All-Star and Gold Glove winner who spent parts of the 2006-07 seasons with the Phillies was dealt to the Houston Astros as part of the Brad Lidge trade?

ANSWERS

1.

Curt Schilling

2.

Roy Halladay and Cliff Lee

3.

Ryne Sandberg

4.

Gio Gonzalez

5.

Scott Rolen

Michael Bourn

NICKNAMES

1. What four-time Phillies All-Star nicknamed "The Bull" hit the only home run of the 1980 NLCS?

2. "Chooch" delivered the first World Series walk-off infield single with his game-winning bases-loaded chopper in Game 3 of the 2008 World Series. Who is he?

3. Referred to as "Wild Thing," what Phillies pitcher served up the World Series-clinching walk off home run in 1993 to Joe Carter of the Toronto Blue Jays?

4. Name the Phillies player nicknamed "Dutch" who was a three-time All-Star winner and 1992 Silver Slugger recipient.

5. What player who pitched for the Phillies in 2007 was coined "El Pulpo," meaning "The Octopus" in Spanish, because he had six fingers on both of his hands?

What Phillie with the alternate alias "The Dandy Little Glove Man" made his lone All-Star appearance in 1995 at The Ballpark in Arlington?

ANSWERS

1.

Greg Luzinski

2.

Carlos Ruiz

3.

Mitch Williams

4.

Darren Daulton

5.

Antonio Alfonseca

Mickey Morandini

THERE'S A DRAFT IN HERE

1. What player was taken first overall out of the University of Miami by the Phillies in the 1998 First-Year Player Draft?

2. Who was selected by the Phillies with the #2 pick in the 1997 First-Year Player Draft but refused to sign, re-entered the draft the next year and was taken by the Cardinals?

3. The Phillies found a diamond in the rough when they drafted what future two-time All-Star outfielder from the Dodgers in the 2004 Rule 5 Draft?

4. What future Cy Young and MVP winner was plucked from the Phillies by the Chicago Cubs in the 1976 Rule 5 Draft, although he would later be re-acquired in 1983?

5. What Phillies outfielder was drafted #1 overall out of high school by the Tampa Bay Devil Rays in 2003?

Former Phillies John Kruk, Doug Glanville and Curt Schilling serve as studio analysts for what hardball highlights television show?

ANSWERS

1.

Pat Burrell

2.

J.D. Drew

3.

Shane Victorino

4.

Willie Hernandez

5.

Delmon Young

Baseball Tonight

LEFTY

1. The Phillies landed a steal when they acquired Steve Carlton from the St. Louis Cardinals in a straight-up trade for whom?

2. Impressively, Carlton won 46 percent of the last-place Phillies games in 1972. How many wins did he record that season?

3. Carlton's 329 wins are the second highest amount for lefties behind what other southpaw pitcher?

4. At his retirement in 1988, Carlton held the record for most Cy Young Awards in a career, which has since been eclipsed. How many did he have?

5. How many no-hitters did Steve Carlton throw?

❄ SEASONAL STUMPER ❄

This one should be considered a gift from Santa: If you can fill in the blank from the holiday flick *A Miracle on __th Street*, then you know the uniform number worn by Roy Halladay. Do you?

ANSWERS

1.

Rick Wise

2.

27

3.

Warren Spahn

4.

Four

5.

None- but he had six one-hitters.

Seasonal Stumper Answer:

34

HOT STOVE

1. This man became baseball's highest-paid player when the Phillies signed him to a four-year, $3.2 million deal in December of 1978. Name him.

2. The Phillies landed a thunderous power bat when they inked what slugger to a six-year $85 million pact in December of 2002?

3. In December of 2010, what pitcher shocked the baseball world by taking less money to return to Philadelphia rather than sign with the New York Yankees?

4. After shelling out a three-year $24 million contract, the Phillies swung-and-missed on what free agent in November of 2006 who posted ERAs around six in his two seasons?

5. In December of 2006, the Phillies signed a free agent outfielder to a one-year $850,000 pact, a player who would blossom into an All-Star in Philly. Who is he?

What third baseman was faced with the daunting task of filling Mike Schmidt's shoes as the Phillies regular third baseman after being acquired in a 1989 trade shortly after Schmidt's retirement?

ANSWERS

1.

Pete Rose

2.

Jim Thome

3.

Cliff Lee

4.

Adam Eaton

5.

Jayson Werth

Charlie Hayes

HARRY THE K

1. Before becoming the Phillies play-by-play commentator in 1971, Harry Kalas worked broadcasts for what other major league team?

2. Kalas was honored with what prestigious award for baseball broadcasters in 2002?

3. What was Kalas' signature home run call?

4. In addition to his baseball notoriety, Kalas was the recognizable voice from what other sports media outlet?

5. After every Phillies victory at Citizens Bank Park, a rendition of what song sung by Kalas is played?

What Phillie seemed to always save his best for the New York Mets, as he swatted 42 home runs and knocked in 104 RBIs against the Metropolitans over the course of his Philadelphia career from 2000-08?

ANSWERS

1.

Houston Astros

2.

Ford C. Frick Award

3.

"Outta here"

4.

NFL Films

5.

"High Hopes"

Pat Burrell

Closing Time

1. Who holds both the Phillies single season saves record with 45 and career saves mark with 112?

2. Who is the only Phillies closer to take home National League Cy Young honors when he did so in 1987?

3. What Phillies reliever is one of only five pitchers in history to have 100 saves, 100 wins and 50 complete games over the course of their career?

4. What pitcher began the 2007 campaign as the Phillies Opening Day starter but became the team's closer by the end of the month, notching 21 saves by season's end?

5. Who set a Phillies pitching record and led the league in games finished with 70 in 2005?

True or False? In four seasons with the Phillies, Cliff Lee compiled a .315 batting average and had 33 home runs.

ANSWERS

1.

Jose Mesa

2.

Steve Bedrosian

3.

Ron Reed

4.

Brett Myers

5.

Billy Wagner

True - Cliff Lee was a catcher and first
baseman from 1921-24 with the Phillies.

Either Or

1. Which World Series-clinching closer has more career saves as a member of the Phillies: Tug McGraw or Brad Lidge?

2. Which Phillies ace amassed more wins during their time in Philadelphia: Robin Roberts or Steve Carlton?

3. In a passing of the torch season for slugging Philadelphia first basemen, which Phillie hit more home runs in 2005: Jim Thome or Ryan Howard?

4. Which face of the Phillies franchise amassed more hits in their Philadelphia careers: Richie Ashburn or Mike Schmidt?

5. Which Phillies hurler recorded more strikeouts in their perfect game performance: Jim Bunning or Roy Halladay?

❄ SEASONAL STUMPER ❄

This Phillie pitcher was born two days after Christmas in 1983 and with the name his parents gave him, you might think he was automatically relegated to Santa's naughty list.

ANSWERS

1.
Brad Lidge (100)

2.
Steve Carlton (241)

3.
Ryan Howard (22)

4.
Mike Schmidt (2,234)

5.
Roy Halladay (11)

Seasonal Stumper Answer:

Cole Hamels

2008 WORLD SERIES

1. In Game 4 of the 2008 NLCS, what pinch-hitter launched a now iconic two-run homer in the eighth inning off of Dodgers closer Jonathan Broxton to break a 5-5 tie?

2. The Phillies got right to work in Game 1 of the World Series against the Tampa Bay Rays when what player hit a two-run home run in the top of the first inning?

3. The Phillies hit four home runs in Game 4, including two of them from Ryan Howard. What Philadelphia pitcher joined in on the fun with a homer of his own?

4. Game 5 was suspended because of rain and resumed on a later day. Was this the only time that's happened in World Series history?

5. Which longtime Phillie hit a double in the bottom of the seventh inning of Game 5 which would end up representing the World Series-clinching run?

What's the last name of the only grandfather-father-son umpires to have worked Phillies postseason games?

ANSWERS

1.

Matt Stairs

2.

Chase Utley

3.

Joe Blanton, becoming the first pitcher to go yard in a Fall Classic game since 1974

4.

Yes

5.

Pat Burrell

Runge- Ed (1977 NLCS), Paul (1993 World Series), and Brian (2008 NLDS)

ALL IN THE FAMILY

1. What Phillies pitcher who was an All-Star in 2003 has a brother who is a major league umpire?

2. What former Phillies manager's father played 27 games for Philadelphia in 1967?

3. What father of a Phillies "Whiz Kid" was inducted into the National Baseball Hall of Fame in 1939?

4. What Phillies 1983 NLCS MVP-winning player's son hit for the cycle in 2006 as a member of the Texas Rangers?

5. What former Phillies catcher was the son of a big leaguer and the father of two others?

Who played for and managed both the Philadelphia Phillies and the New York Mets?

ANSWERS

1.

   Randy Wolf

2.

   Terry Francona

3.

   George Sisler (son Dick)

4.

   Gary Matthews

5.

   Bob Boone – father, Ray Boone;
   two sons, Aaron and Bret

Dallas Green

THE PHILLIE PHANATIC

1.

The Phillie Phanatic made its
Phillies debut during what
season: 1968, 1978 or 1988?

2.

What brother and sister
tandem did the Phillie
Phanatic replace as Phillies mascot?

3.

According to his profile, where is
the Phillie Phanatic's birthplace?

4.

The Phillie Phanatic had a
rivalry with what legendary Los
Angeles Dodgers manager?

5.

In 2005, the Phillie Phanatic was part of
the inaugural class to what institution?

In Game 4 of the 1981 NLDS, what Phillie
pinch-hitting for Tug McGraw in the bottom of the
tenth inning hit a walk-off home run to force a
winner-take-all Game 5 versus the Montreal Expos?

ANSWERS

1.

1978

2.

Philadelphia Phil and Philadelphia Phyllis

3.

Galapagos Islands

4.

Tommy Lasorda

5.

The Mascot Hall of Fame

George Vukovich

SCHMITTY

1. Mike Schmidt won more MVPs than any other third basemen in history. How many times was he named the National League's Most Valuable Player?

2. On April 17, 1976, Schmidt became just the 10th player in major league history, at the time, and third Phillie to do what in one game?

3. Schmidt had a magical 1980 season in which he became one of just five players to win what two awards in the same season?

4. Mostly known for his potent bat, Schmidt was also a slick-fielding third baseman, taking home how many Gold Glove Awards over the course of his career?

5. On April 18, 1987, in Pittsburgh, Schmidt swatted a three-run homer in the top of the ninth for his milestone 500th home run. What Pirates pitcher did Schmidt victimize?

❄ SEASONAL STUMPER ❄

Citizens Bank Park played host to what New Year's Day sporting tradition in 2012?

ANSWERS

1.

Three (1980, 1981 and 1986)

2.

Hit four home runs

3.

Regular season MVP and
World Series MVP

4.

10

5.

Don Robinson

Seasonal Stumper Answer:

The 2012 NHL Winter Classic between the
Philadelphia Flyers and New York Rangers

Senator Bunning

1. In 1964, Jim Bunning tossed a perfect game against the New York Mets at Shea Stadium on what holiday?

2. Bunning led the National League in strikeouts in 1967 with more or less than 250 Ks?

3. Bunning is one of only five hurlers to throw a no-hitter in both the AL and NL. For what American League team did Bunning pitch a no-hitter in 1958?

4. After 15 years on the National Baseball Hall of Fame ballot, Bunning finally made it into the Hall in 1996 by what method?

5. After his playing days, Bunning began a career in politics and served as a United States Senator for what state?

On May 20, 1951, the Phillies swept a doubleheader against the Pirates as what player had four hits in each game?

ANSWERS

1.

Father's Day

2.

More- 253

3.

Detroit Tigers

4.

He was voted in by the
Veteran's Committee.

5.

Kentucky

Richie Ashburn

OLD PETE

1. True or False? Grover Cleveland Alexander was a 30-game winner for three consecutive seasons?

2. Alexander tied George Bradley's record for most shutouts in a single season in 1916 when he pitched how many scoreless complete games: 8, 12, or 16?

3. In 1915 and 1916, Alexander captured the National League pitching Triple Crown with the Phillies by leading the league in what three categories?

4. Alexander and what other Hall of Fame pitcher are tied for the National League record for career wins with 373 victories each?

5. What famous actor portrayed Alexander in the biographical film *The Winning Team*?

What Cincinnati Reds player's steal of home plate against the Phillies on September 21, 1964, triggered Philadelphia's historic 1964 late season collapse, as the Phils went on to lose the next ten games and the National League pennant?

ANSWERS

1.

True, from the Phillies
pennant-winning 1915
season through 1917

2.

16

3.

ERA, wins and strikeouts

4.

Christy Mathewson

5.

Ronald Reagan

Chico Ruiz

Second Guessing

1. With his no-hitter against the Cincinnati Reds in the 2010 NLDS, what pitcher became just the second player to toss a no-hitter in the postseason?

2. What player inducted into the National Baseball Hall of Fame as part of its second induction class was the first Phillies player voted into Cooperstown?

3. What longtime Phillies pitcher is second behind Steve Carlton for career walks in Philly history?

4. In 1983, Cal Ripken, Jr. became the first player to follow a Rookie of the Year Award-winning season with MVP honors the next year. Who was second to accomplish the feat in 2006?

5. With his Gold Glove at third base in 2011, what Phillie became the second player to win the award at two different positions, with the other coming at second base?

What Phillies role player etched his name into Phillies playoff lore when he blasted a three-run homer coming off the bench to pinch hit for Cole Hamels in Game 3 of the 2011 NLDS against the St. Louis Cardinals?

Answers

1.

Roy Halladay

2.

Nap Lajoie

3.

Chris Short (762)

4.

Ryan Howard

5.

Placido Polanco

Ben Francisco

THE HOOSIER HAMMER

1. Chuck Klein won the NL home run title in 1929 by slugging his 43rd homer in the final game in a head-to-head matchup against what slugger who finished with 42 dingers?

2. Klein became the first Phillie to be awarded what honor in 1932?

3. Although he finished second in the 1933 MVP voting, Klein pulled off an arguably even more impressive achievement. What was that?

4. Klein showcased his cannon of an arm in the outfield by setting the single season record in what defensive category in 1930?

5. In 1936, Klein became the first National Leaguer in the 20th century to achieve what single game feat?

❄ SEASONAL STUMPER ❄

"If a horse won't eat it, I don't want to play on it."
What former Phillie said that back in
the days of artificial turf?
(Hint: He has the same last name as the star
of the holiday flick *The Santa Clause.*)

ANSWERS

1.

Mel Ott

2.

National League MVP

3.

National League Triple Crown

4.

Assists, 44

5.

Hit 4 home runs in one game

Seasonal Stumper Answer:

Dick Allen

(Tim Allen is the actor.)

THE BANK

1. Prior to the opening of Citizens Bank Park in 2004, the Phillies called what ballpark their home for 32 years?

2. Who hit the first home run in Citizens Bank Park on April 12, 2004, which doubled as the Phillies first hit in their new digs?

3. On June 25, 2010, Ryan Howard became the first DH in a regular season game in a National League ballpark. What's going on here?

4. The longest home run hit in Citizens Bank Park history was a 496-foot shot to center field. Who hit it?

5. What happens in right center field every time the Phillies hit a home run at Citizens Bank Park?

On July 17, 1918, the Phillies played their longest game ever against the Chicago Cubs. How many innings did the contest last?

ANSWERS

1.

Veterans Stadium

2.

Bobby Abreu

3. Because of the G-20 Summit in Toronto, for security reasons, the Phillies road series against the Blue Jays was moved to Citizens Bank Park. Philadelphia was the "visitor."

4.

Ryan Howard

5.

A replica Liberty Bell rings.

21 (The Phillies lost, 2-1.)

HIS PLAYING DAYS ARE NUMBERED

In their history, the Phillies have officially
retired five of their players' uniform numbers.
Match up each with his number.

1. Richie Ashburn   a. 1

2. Jim Bunning   b. 14

3. Steve Carlton   c. 20

4. Robin Roberts   d. 32

5. Mike Schmidt   e. 36

Who was the last Phillies player to wear #42
before Major League Baseball retired the number
across the league in honor of Jackie Robinson?

ANSWERS

1.
   a

2.
   b

3.
   d

4.
   e

5.
   c

Toby Borland

BRIEF STAYS

1. Reuniting with Pete Rose, what two members of Cincinnati's vaunted "Big Red Machine" teams played one season for the Phillies in 1983?

2. What Hall of Fame slugging first baseman, who starred for the cross-town A's earlier in his career, played the final season of his career for the Phillies in 1945?

3. What Hall of Fame three-time World Series-winning manager spent the only season of his playing career with the Phillies in 1959?

4. As his career wound down, what Hall of Famer and owner of the major league record for RBIs in a single season logged 20 at-bats for the Phillies in 1934?

5. In 2009, what former All-Star pitcher made his Phillies debut in August and went 5-1, contributing to Philly's second straight NL pennant and World Series appearance?

Scott Rolen hit the first home run in the history of what brand new Texas ballpark in 2000?

ANSWERS

1.

Joe Morgan and Tony Perez

2.

Jimmie Foxx

3.

Sparky Anderson

4.

Hack Wilson

5.

Pedro Martinez

Enron Field (Now known as Minute Maid Park)

SILVER SLUGGERS

1. The Silver Slugger Award is given out every year to the best hitter at each position in both leagues. The Phillies have had Silver Sluggers at every position except where?

2. What Phillies player has won the most National League Silver Sluggers at his position?

3. In his 1993 Silver Slugger-winning season, what Phillies player finished second to Barry Bonds in National League MVP balloting?

4. What two-time Silver Slugging second baseman knocked in the eventual game-winning run in Game 5 of the 1980 World Series with a single in the ninth vs. the Royals?

5. What Phillie led the National League in triples with 15 in 1987 when he was awarded the Silver Slugger as a second baseman?

❄ SEASONAL STUMPER ❄

Here's some simple holiday math: Add the number of French Hens in *The Twelve Days of Christmas* to the number of letters in the French word for Christmas and you have the number of NL pennants the Phillies have won in their history. And that number is…?

ANSWERS

1.

Pitcher

2.

Mike Schmidt

3.

Lenny Dykstra

4.

Manny Trillo

5.

Juan Samuel

Seasonal Stumper Answer:

3 (French Hens) + 4 (letters in Noel) =
7 (Phillies pennants)

WHO SAID IT?

1. After resigning as Phillies manager after Opening Day in 1960, who explained his rationale for stepping down by saying, "I'm 49 years old and I'd like to live to be 50"?

2. Upon retiring during the 1989 season, who said, "I could ask the Phillies to keep me on to add to my statistics, but my love for the game wouldn't let me do that"?

3. In reference to the Phillies finishing last in 1992, who said, "I'd rather be in a prison cell with Mike Tyson, and let him beat my butt all day long, than go through that again"?

4. After being booed by Philadelphia fans, what former Phillie manager said, "I've been released five times, I'm bald and I have a big nose. I'll make it through this"?

5. "One time, I got pulled over at 4 a.m. I was fined seventy-five dollars for being intoxicated and four-hundred for being with the Phillies." What 1960s undistinguished catcher said it?

He piloted the Phillies from 1960-68 and spent a total of 26 seasons managing without ever winning a pennant, the longest stretch in baseball history. Can you name him?

Answers

1.

Eddie Sawyer

2.

Mike Schmidt

3.

John Kruk

4.

Terry Francona

5.

Bob Uecker

Gene Mauch

WEB GEMS

1. What Phillies shortstop, who won a Gold Glove Award in 1963, was also a coach on the staff of the Phillies 1980 World Series Championship team?

2. What pitcher's string of 16 straight Gold Gloves was snapped while he was a member of the Phillies, with his final two awards coming in 1976 and 1977 in Philadelphia?

3. According to broadcasting legend Harry Kalas, "Two-thirds of the Earth is covered by water, the other one-third is covered by _____."

4. What former Phillies first baseman, a 1966 Gold Glove winner, became the first African-American team play-by-play announcer in 1971 for the Yankees?

5. In the final year of his career and lone season in Philadelphia, what former MVP-winning pitcher was awarded his eighth Gold Glove in 1964?

In 1987, what Phillie became the first player in major league history to reach double figures in doubles, triples, home runs and stolen bases in each of his first four major league seasons?

ANSWERS

1.

Bobby Wine

2.

Jim Kaat

3.

Garry Maddox

4.

Bill White

5.

Bobby Shantz

Juan Samuel

J-ROLL

1. Jimmy Rollins burst onto the scene in 2001 by tying with Juan Pierre for the National League lead in what category in his rookie season?

2. Over the span of the 2005-2006 seasons, Rollins broke Ed Delahanty's Phillies record for the longest hitting streak. In how many consecutive games did Rollins get a hit?

3. With the Phillies down to their last out and trailing by a run to the Dodgers, Rollins came to the plate in the bottom of the ninth in Game 4 of the 2009 NLCS. What did he do?

4. After batting .417 and swiping four bases for Team USA in 2009, Rollins was named the shortstop for what international tournament honorary squad?

5. In 2004, Rollins made history by becoming the first player to hit the first inside the park home runs in two ballparks' histories. In what two new ballparks did Rollins do this?

Who was considered Steve Carlton's personal catcher?

ANSWERS

1.

Stolen bases, with 46

2.

38

3.

He laced a walk off two-run
double into right center field.

4.

All-World Baseball Classic Team

5.

Citizens Bank Park and Petco Park

Tim McCarver

Award Tour

1. In 1983, the National League Champion Phillies pitching staff boasted the league Cy Young Award winner and the Rolaids Relief Man of the Year. Who were they?

2. In 1964, what Phillies third baseman led the league in runs, triples, extra base hits and total bases, easily taking home National League Rookie of the Year honors?

3. After two underwhelming seasons with the Astros, what Phillies reliever rebounded with a stellar 2008 campaign in Philadelphia to win the NL Comeback Player of the Year?

4. What Phillies first-year pitcher was honored as the 1957 NL Rookie of the Year after winning 19 games and leading the league in strikeouts with 188?

5. During the 2009 postseason, what Phillie garnered NLCS MVP honors when he tied Lou Gehrig's record for consecutive playoff games with an RBI?

❄ Seasonal stumpeR ❄

True or false? The Phillies once held Spring Training in Christmas, Florida.

ANSWERS

1.

John Denny and Al Holland

2.

Dick Allen

3.

Brad Lidge

4.

Jack Sanford

5.

Ryan Howard (eight straight games)

Seasonal Stumper Answer:

False- But there is a Christmas in Florida, about 130 miles east of the Phillies Spring Training camp in Clearwater.

DOWN ON THE FARM

1. Who was the Pacific Coast League manager of the year in 2010, *Baseball America's* Minor League Manager of the year in 2011, and became a big league pilot in 2013?

2. Following his call up from the Iron Pigs, what Phillies outfielder hit a three-run homer off Andy Pettitte at Yankee Stadium in his first MLB game in May of 2009?

3. Called up by the Phillies in 1982 from the Oklahoma City 89ers, he went on to play until the age of 49 in 2008, the oldest regular position player ever. Who is he?

4. What two future Phillies led the Double-A affiliate Reading Phillies to an Eastern League co-championship in 2001 with the team lead in home runs and wins, respectively?

5. What former Phillies prospect included in the 2009 Cliff Lee blockbuster represented Philadelphia three times for the World Team in the Futures Games from 2006-08?

After years of toiling in the minors, what Phillies catcher finally cracked the major leagues in 2006 at the age of 33?

ANSWERS

1.

Ryne Sandberg, who
replaced Charlie Manuel

2.

John Mayberry, Jr.

3.

Julio Franco

4.

Marlon Byrd (28 home runs)
and Carlos Silva (15 wins)

5.

Carlos Carrasco

Chris Coste

MIDSUMMER CLASSICS

1. The Phillies have hosted All-Star Games in 1952, 1976 and 1996. Who was the only Phillies All-Star representative in 1996 when the game was played at Veterans Stadium?

2. In 1964 at Shea Stadium, who became the only Phillies player to be named All-Star Game MVP when he hit a walk off home run for the National Leaguers?

3. What Phillie was the starting pitcher for the National League All-Stars in 1993 at Oriole Park at Camden Yards?

4. What Phillie faced off against Randy Johnson in the 1993 All-Star Game when The Big Unit famously fired a fastball over his head to start off the at-bat?

5. What two Phillies were the winning pitchers in back-to-back All-Star Games in 1994 and 1995?

Who are the only two Phillie pitchers to strike out 300 batters in a season?

ANSWERS

1.

Ricky Bottalico

2.

Johnny Callison

3.

Terry Mullholland

4.

John Kruk

5.

Doug Jones and Heathcliff
Slocumb, respectively

Steve Carlton (310 strikeouts in 1972) and
Curt Schilling (319 in 1997 and 300 in 1998)

Multi-Sport Studs

1. What NFL All-Pro running back and Heisman Trophy recipient was drafted by the Phillies in the eighth round of the 1995 draft?

2. What Phillies All-Star selection in 1959 also won three NBA championships with the Boston Celtics from 1959-61?

3. Legendary Phillie Robin Roberts was the captain of the basketball team for what college program?

4. What Pro Football Hall of Fame and two-time Super Bowl-winning coach was offered a contract by the Phillies but declined to sign with the team?

5. What Hall of Fame pitcher who began his career with the Phillies also played basketball for the Harlem Globetrotters from 1967-69?

What left-handed reliever won two games for the Phillies in the 2008 World Series, including the title-clinching Game 5?

ANSWERS

1.
Ricky Williams

2.
Gene Conley

3.
Michigan State University

4.
Bill Parcells

5.
Ferguson Jenkins

J.C. Romero

LAST LICKS

1. In 1932, what Phillie became the last player to lead the NL in home runs and stolen bases in the same season, when he led the senior circuit with 38 homers and 20 steals?

2. What Phillies player hit a home run against the Rockies in April of 2009 that would be Harry Kalas' last home run call?

3. In a game against the Montreal Expos on June 28, 2004, what Philadelphia third baseman became the last Phillie to hit for the cycle?

4. What Phillie ended a 2009 game against the New York Mets by becoming the last player in major league baseball history to turn an unassisted triple play?

5. In the second-to-last game of the 2003 season, what player hit the last home run at Veterans Stadium?

What stadium's right field wall featured a soap advertisement which read "The Phillies Use LIFEBUOY", prompting the often-said wisecrack, "and they still stink"?

ANSWERS

1.
Chuck Klein

2.
Matt Stairs

3.
David Bell

4.
Eric Bruntlett

5.
Jim Thome

The Baker Bowl, home to the Phillies from 1887-1938

TEAM TRIVIA

Okay, so you think you know the Phillies pretty well, but how about their opponents? See if you can identify each of the major league teams from the following questions.

1. What team has won the most games in a regular season since the turn of the century?

2. Minnie Minoso made a brief appearance for this team in 1980, making it the fifth decade that he played Major League Baseball, the only player since 1900 to do so. Name the club.

3. This Hall of Famer's #29 has been retired by the Angels and one other club. Can you name the player and the team?

4. In 1959, Harvey Haddix threw the longest perfect game in major league history, 12 innings. Unfortunately he lost the no-hitter and the game, 1-0, in the 13th to the Milwaukee Braves. Haddix was pitching for what team?

5. What team played at Wrigley Field in its first year of existence?

At Connie Mack Stadium on August 17, 1957, a fan was hit with two foul balls by the same batter. What Phillie committed the foul play?

6. What club became the first wild card team in major league history to win a World Series, in 1997?

7. What team changed its name for a while during the cold war with Russia?

8. Who did the St. Louis Browns become?

9. In 1965, Bert Campaneris became the first major leaguer to play an inning at each of the nine defensive positions in one game. With what team did he achieve this feat?

10. This club is one of only two teams to originate in California. They have never won a World Series and are the only MLB team that's never had a pitcher throw a no-hitter. Name them.

11. Wade Boggs was the first player to hit a home run for his 3,000th hit. What team was he playing for at the time?

12. In 1965, they became the first MLB team to play their home games in an indoor park.

Richie Ashburn- His first foul ball struck spectator Alice Roth and broke her nose. As she was being carried off on a stretcher, she was hit with another foul, breaking a bone in her knee.

13. Andres Galarraga hit one of the longest homers in big league history for this team- a 529-foot tape measure job against the Marlins at Pro Player Stadium in 1997.

14. Name the last major league franchise to relocate from one city to another.

15. On September 10, 1963, three Alou brothers- Jesus, Matty, and Felipe -all batted in a row for what team?

16. The New York Yankees have won the most World Series. What team is a distant second?

17. The first African-American manager in MLB history was hired by what team?

18. What team was managed by its owner for a single game?

19. Who was selected the 2004 "Sportsman of the Year" by *Sports Illustrated*?

20. What franchise won a World Series title in only its fourth year of existence, 2001?

David Raymond owns what distinction in Phillies lore?

21. What team has lost the most games in a single season?

22. When this team's state of the art baseball only ballpark opened in 1962, it had no water fountains! Name the team.

23. Not only was Harmon Killebrew the first Minnesota Twin to make it to the Hall of Fame- he was also the first player on what other club to make it to the Hall?

24. What team, since the inception of the American League in 1901, became the first club to switch leagues?

25. Name the team that holds the record for most home runs in a game in major league history.

26. Its present owner is the founder of Little Caesar's pizza. Its former owner is the founder of Domino's pizza. What team is this?

27. Harry Steinfeldt is the answer to the question "Who was the third baseman?" of the famous infield on what team?

He was the first Phillie Phanatic.

28. Name the only team in Major League Baseball history to win five consecutive World Series.

29. Hall of Famer Ted Williams was the very first manager for what team in 1972?

In 1985, what Phillie became the first player in major league history to hit two home runs in the first inning?

ANSWERS

1. The Seattle Mariners, 116, in 2001 (tying the MLB record with the Chicago Cubs, who also won 116 way back in 1906)

2. Chicago White Sox

3. Rod Carew, by the Twins

4. Pittsburgh Pirates

5. The Los Angeles Angels, in 1961- Wrigley Field in Los Angeles, that is. (The Cubs played at the West Side Grounds in Chicago before moving into *the* Wrigley Field.)

6. Miami (then Florida) Marlins

7. The Cincinnati Reds (as in Soviets) changed their name to the Red Legs.

8. The Baltimore Orioles

9. The Oakland Athletics

10. San Diego Padres

11. The Tampa Bay Rays (then Devil Rays)

Von Hayes- His second dinger was a grand slam that climaxed a nine-run first inning en route to a 26-7 shellacking of the Mets.

12. Houston Astros

13. Colorado Rockies

14. The Montreal Expos, who moved from
    Canada to become the Washington Nationals

15. The San Francisco Giants- Jesus and Matty were
    both pinch-hitters before eldest brother Felipe
    stepped up. Five days later they would make
    history again, playing in the same outfield together.

16. St. Louis Cardinals

17. Cleveland Indians, in 1975, who hired Frank
    Robinson

18. Atlanta Braves- With his team in the midst of a
    16-game losing streak, owner Ted Turner decided to
    manage things himself and did so in a 2-1 loss to
    the Pirates. MLB rules do not allow owners to
    manage, so that was Turner's first and last game at
    the helm.

19. The entire Boston Red Sox team

20. Arizona Diamondbacks

21. The 1962 New York Mets who, in their first year,
    lost 120 games (40-120)

❄ SEASONAL STUMPER ❄

Here's a gift from Santa:
If you know how many days are in the 12
Days of Christmas, then you know the
answer to this question- What number did
Ryan Howard originally wear when
he joined the Phillies in 2004?

22. Los Angeles Dodgers (Dodger Stadium was without water fountains, an "oversight" according to owner Walter O'Malley.)

23. Kansas City Royals (Killebrew played his final season, 1975, with the Royals.)

24. The Milwaukee Brewers - They moved from the AL Central to the NL Central in 1998.

25. Toronto Blue Jays (10 homers in an 18-3 win over the Orioles on September 14, 1987)

26. Detroit Tigers (Mike Ilitch and Tom Monaghan are the current and former owners, respectively.)

27. The Chicago Cubs, whose famed "Tinker to Evers to Chance" infield double play combination featured Steinfeldt at third

28. The New York Yankees, from 1949-53

29. Texas Rangers

Seasonal Stumper Answer:

Merry Christmas!